THE
THERAPIST'S GUIDE
TO
BEING PREGNANT

A planner, timeline, and guide
for therapist parents-to-be

Kara Bolling
MSW, LCSW-C

COPYRIGHT

ISBN: 978-1-7343158-0-6

Library of Congress Control Number: 2019918788

Cover art and book design by Robert "Bobby" Wildermuth. www.robertbobbyart.com

Printed by IngramSparks, in the United States of America.

First printing edition 2019.

Published by Two Suns Healing, LLC: Baltimore, Maryland

www.karabolling.com

To my guys — Cameron, Gil, & Cyrus — I love you.

Thank You

Acknowledgements

Thanks to Sara Mindel and all the women of the 2016 Sensorimotor Psychotherapy training in Washington, D.C. for their emotional support, kind guidance, and celebration of my entry into motherhood.

Thanks to Sarah Branson, Brittany Coffman, Carla Paisley, Heather Brown, Dr. Pam Woodward, Yeshe Clarke, Dr. Samantha DuFlo, Jessie Bernstein, and Keri Nola, among others, for their loving and empowering support for all of me during my second pregnancy.

Thank you to my most-adorable boys for coming into my life and growing me and for all the tickles and laughs and drooly kisses. Thank you to my handsome husband for making my business and my work important to him.

CONTENTS

Preface / i

Introduction / iii

FIRST TRIMESTER

First Things First: Survive the First Trimester / 3

Hurdles to Overcome, What If You're Unexpectedly Pregnant, The Uncertainty Of the First Trimester, Self-Care for Pregnancy, Short-Term Disability Insurance

Let's Break This Down: Morning Sickness / 6

Let's Break This Down: Financial Planning For Taking Leave / 12

First Trimester Checklist & Timeline / 17

SECOND TRIMESTER

Sometime Later: Client Work In the Second Trimester / 21

The Impact Of Your Pregnancy, Preparing For Post-Announcement, Looking Ahead to the Fourth Trimester, When to Stop Taking New Clients, Control Is an Illusion: So Plan for Early Labor, The Parental Leave Release of Info, Making Big Decisions

Let's Break This Down: Deciding When To Break the News / 22

Let's Break This Down: The Announcement / 28

Let's Break This Down: When To Carry On With the Business of Your Business / 37

Let's Break This Down: Talking With Potential Clients / 42

Second Trimester Checklist & Timeline / 51

THIRD TRIMESTER

Nearing the End: Wrapping Things Up In the Third Trimester / 57

Winding Down Your Clinical Work, Have I Talked Enough About Self-Care, Termination, Transitioning Clients to Other Providers, When to Transition, Documentation, Your Last Day of Work, "How are you doing?"

Third Trimester Checklist & Timeline / 69

Conclusion / 71

Resources / 74

References / 80

CONGRATS!

Preface

Therapists, psychotherapists, and counselors working with individuals, couples, families, and/or groups (especially those in private practice) — welcome to this book and congratulations on your pregnancy! This will likely be a joyful, exhausting, indigestion-filled, very human time in your life — a time to celebrate, prepare, rest, and reach out for your own support. If you're anything like me, you got into this business because you're really good at supporting others. The goal of this book is to support you.

If you're a therapist whose partner is expecting and you're wondering how new parenthood and parental leave might affect your own work, welcome and congratulations to you too! If you or your partner are not pregnant yet but are hoping to be soon — look at you, being all prepared and stuff. I'm wishing all of you the best in navigating the ups and downs of pregnancy, childbirth, and the postpartum period.

"The state of relaxation of the mouth and jaw is directly correlated to the ability of the cervix, the vagina, and the anus to open to full capacity."

Ina May Gaskin, Ina May's Guide to Childbirth

THIS IS ME

Introduction

When I discovered I was pregnant with my first child, I was working part-time in private practice and nearly full-time in an agency. I had a lot of questions about how pregnancy would change my life and my practice, and I needed answers right away. However, I also wanted privacy in the first trimester — I wasn't ready to reveal my pregnancy to everyone — and there were very few resources in print or online to anonymously seek out the answers to my questions.

Luckily, I had some trusted friends in the business to whom I discretely reached out to help me think through how best to prepare my clients for the change that was about to happen. What came back to me time and time again was how important it was to take care of myself. We've all used the oxygen mask metaphor at least once in our sessions, right? In case you haven't, here it is: when you fly, the attendants always say, "If you're traveling with a child or someone who needs help, put your mask on first and then help the other person." Well, news flash, friend, this applies to you too! Take care of yourself so that you have what you need to be able to take care of your family, your clients, and your work.

As I began to write this little book, I was a couple years into a full-time private practice and embarking on a second pregnancy. I had plenty of therapist-mom friends, but not many who had been in this same professional situation when they had their kids. I searched around online again hoping to discover books or articles that would refresh my memory and maybe even speak to how the circumstances of my life were a little different now. Coming up with precious few resources that were mostly dry and dull, I decided to share my questions, ideas, and stories with you. Writing this book helped me prepare and then relax into my decisions and, pregnant people, we all need to find ways to relax into this messy, happy time.

I'm a somatic therapist, currently training in Sensorimotor Psychotherapy, which has the following principles as its foundation (Kurtz, 2015): Organicity (people have innate wisdom and innate capacity for growth and change), Non-Violence (people deserve to be held in compassion and non-judgment), Unity (people deserve to be collaboratively involved in their own growth and decision-making because we are all human, all connected), Mind-Body-Spirit Holism (the body, the mind, and the spirit are all connected), and Mindfulness & Presence (change and wellness are possible when people can honor the moment of having an experience while observing that experience with curiosity). These principles alone have changed the way I work and have improved my connections with clients. I have also consulted these principles when choosing how to write this book, and I hope it shows.

The ideas in this book might not ring true for each of you reading it; we all have different orientations to life and to our work as therapists, social workers, and counselors. Although I do take positions and give advice in this book, I hope you will hear my words as a sharing of experience rather than a knowing-what's-best-for-you-better-than-you-do. Somewhere inside you, you know what you need. I see you and I honor your differences and your process.

Let me also take a minute to acknowledge my privilege. I'm a white, cisgender, straight woman. I haven't encountered much discrimination in life or many obstacles in building my business. I'm married and my husband works full-time and contributes the greater share of household income. I live just outside a major city and I have access to clientele who can afford to pay me directly for our work. I acknowledge that many people face greater professional and financial obstacles than I have. Though this edition of the book is written largely from my perspective, it's my goal to address issues of privilege and social justice more explicitly in a second edition.

This book is written with pregnant therapists in mind. However, for therapist-partners of pregnant people, there will hopefully be ways this pregnancy and especially parenthood will affect you too (of course there will!). I aim to speak to your questions and concerns also.

This book is organized into three sections corresponding to each trimester of pregnancy. At the end of each section, there is a checklist to help you stay on track. The "Let's Break This Down" sections will help you think through specific action steps and then provide spaces to jot down your own thoughts. "The Over-Share" sections are places where I share my own stories, (my "self-disclosures", if you will). Now let's get down to business!

FIRST TRIMESTER

"There is such a special sweetness in being able to participate in creation."

Pamela S. Nadav

First Things First:

Survive the First Trimester

The first trimester begins at conception and lasts until the 14th week of pregnancy. Everyone has a different constellation of body experiences during the first trimester — fatigue, nausea, vomiting, headache, or sometimes nothing at all. Although you might experience changes in your body, you might not want much to change in your practice.

Hurdles to Overcome

For many mothers-to-be (and their partners), the first trimester brings some, if not all, of the following:

- exhaustion (I won't tell you to rest because literally everyone else will)

- caffeine withdrawal, if you choose (a cuppa per day is a-okay, they say)

- nausea. vomiting. indigestion. "the burps". (maybe this last one was just me?)

- endless glasses of water, endless trips to the bathroom (this pretty much continues throughout pregnancy)

- leaving your glee (or your dread) about being pregnant outside the office door (or at least well-contained as you make space for your clients)

- feeling all the bodily woes and going to work anyway (and sometimes… not going)

- keeping your pregnancy a secret (as you do with most of your personal details)

You might not want to take that pregnancy test at the beginning of a work day. There can be a lot of feelings to sift through. If you're like me, big emotions escape your face without your permission and it can take Herculean effort to contain it. The first time I got pregnant I took a pregnancy test right after a lunch break, immediately felt equal parts excited and worried that my husband and I weren't ready yet, and then spent the rest of the afternoon trying to master my emotions while sitting with clients. The second time I got pregnant, I waited until my day off.

What If You're Unexpectedly Pregnant

Did this pregnancy take you by surprise? Having some feelings about it that are difficult to put your finger on? Even if you planned or fought for this pregnancy, all the feelings may show up and prove difficult to sort through. This might just be the right time to go (back) to therapy for yourself. Individual work, couples work, family therapy, therapy for partners of the pregnant — get the support you need.

The Uncertainty of the First Trimester

Content Warning: Pregnancy loss

"It's always possible that I'll have a miscarriage... It's always possible that I'll have a miscarriage...," I often said to myself in my first trimesters, trying to desensitize myself to worried thoughts.

No, you don't want to think about this possibility, but it's an unavoidable reality of pregnancy that's more likely during the first trimester. For this reason and a few others that I'll mention later in the book, wait to let your clients know about your pregnancy until you've reached the second trimester. It doesn't have to be at the beginning of the second trimester, but it makes sense to talk about it with your clients before you've really started to show, before there's an elephant in the room (not literally, you're glowing).

If you do end up having a miscarriage at some point during this pregnancy, it may be little consolation that it happens more than we would like to think. Take such good care of yourself and reach out for support in whatever ways feel right to you (there are some resources listed at the end of this book).

Let's Break This Down:
Morning Sickness

Imagine you are sitting with a client who is distraught about a recent breakup, the loss of a job, the death of a loved one. You are present, so aware of their pain, fear, sadness — and then you are aware of something else entirely. Your body did not get the memo that this client needs you right now. Your body has decided that now is the time to lose your lunch. How do you get yourself from point a: the office, to point b: the bathroom, in a way that minimizes disruption for the client? How do you balance the importance of honest communication and the importance of boundaries? Consider this:

- tell your client at the beginning of the session that you're not feeling great and it's your intention to be as present as possible

- I'm sorry, I'm suddenly not feeling well, I need to grab a drink of water...

- (or even just:) please excuse me, I need to step out for a moment...

Your Thoughts

What might you say when morning sickness strikes?

_____

_____

_____

_____

_____

_____

_____

_____

_____

Morning sickness and other first trimester woes might rock your world, make you feel like you don't have your bearings, make you feel less than effective in your work.

Be kind to yourself. Get good rest, remember to breathe calmly, drink some nice tea, and take good care of yourself.

One day it will all be different.

Self-Care for Pregnancy

How many of us recommend massage, yoga, acupuncture, etc. to our clients and then when it comes to ourselves, we think, "I'm still not ready to pay for that," or "I can never find the time!" If there was ever a right time, pregnant people and even partners of pregnant people, it is now. Pregnancy, labor and delivery, and the postpartum period all put different stressors on the body that if not properly cared for, can haunt our health for the rest of our days (dun-dun-dun!). You deserve to feel as good as you can while sharing your body with your future babe. Massage can help with the aches and pains of pregnancy and can help you get better sleep. Yoga is low impact exercise that can help you relax and get your blood, chi, and breath flowing. Acupuncture can help you improve circulation, reduce stress, and reduce nausea (and hip tip: some insurance plans will cover acupuncture if it's treating your nausea).

But if your right to feel your best and healthiest during pregnancy isn't enough to persuade you to build in some more self-care now, consider that the way your body feels and functions while carrying your baby can also impact labor and delivery, which can also impact postpartum healing. Yoga is great for building strength and practicing tolerance for discomfort. Acupuncture can help with baby's position in your belly. Massage and acupuncture can help bring on labor if that bun's been cooking too long. Prenatal chiropractic care can help with the position of your sacrum and pelvis in preparation for birth. Pelvic floor physical therapy can help you tone your pelvic muscles and perineum. All of these and more provide huge benefits for postpartum healing as well.

Now, therapy… I don't have to tell a bunch of therapists about the benefits of therapy, so I won't. Some of you are already seeing your own therapists, because you have needs and you practice what you preach. The rest of you know you're a human too and sometimes you need extra support and sometimes you've got some issues to work through. #endmentalhealthstigma, and all that.

News flash, to all you highly competent helpers and healers: You're a human too.

One way to access these resources is to spend a pretty penny on them, but that's not the only way. Search for prenatal yoga videos online, and there are several free resources. More and more community acupuncture clinics are popping up, where community sessions cost much less than individual sessions. Prenatal chiropractic care, pelvic floor physical therapy, and mental health therapy are typically covered by insurance plans. You might find low cost massage by participating

in a massage school clinic when students are learning about prenatal/
reproductive systems, or, if you are partnered, you might ask your
partner to care for you by giving you a weekly massage. Be creative.

What are some other self-care strategies that you love and/or that
cost nothing?

_____

_____

_____

_____

_____

_____

_____

_____

_____

_____

_____

_____

The Over-Share

During my first pregnancy, I was a penny-pinching fool hoarding away as much money as I could. No, we were not going to pay for a doula, we'd do it ourselves (yeesh!). No, we could not afford acupuncture or massage. I went to a minimum number of chiropractic sessions, but then I decided the copay was too much. Baby #1 was perfect, but also got into a sunny-side-up position and didn't progress quickly enough for the doctor, and I ended up having the cesarean delivery I didn't want under circumstances that didn't have me convinced it was necessary.

During my second pregnancy, I started prenatal yoga in my first trimester (while nauseous as heck) and massage, acupuncture, and chiropractic care in my second. We hired a fantastic doula and a home-birth midwifery team (not advocating home- over hospital-birth here, but it did come with a LOT more support, and I didn't have to drive anywhere for prenatal care appointments, they all happened in my home). I found a therapist to help me process my first birth, fears about the upcoming birth, and my discomfort with needing to ask for help (I'll admit it). Baby #2 was also perfect, but I pushed him out through only 4 contractions (okay, that's not the whole story, but it sums it up). I can't promise that practicing self-care will gift you the birth you want, but for me there was peace in knowing I was doing everything I could.

Let's Break This Down:
Financial Planning for Taking Leave

Those of you who are self-employed and planning to return to work after maternity leave will still have financial responsibilities to your business while you're out on leave, right? Most of us feelers and healers are also really-super-comfortable with numbers too, right? Here's some food for thought. Especially if you have little to no savings in your practice these days (you're still getting off the ground, a lot of recent CEU spending needs, recent investments in web design/management, etc.), go through this worksheet as early in this pregnancy as you can:

- How many months do you plan to be away on leave? Add 1 for the professional and personal expenses you will have during the first month of your return to work.

Months Of Leave + 1: _____

- What are the ongoing monthly professional and personal expenses that will continue while you're away? (rent, marketing, electronic medical record (EMR) systems, subscription services, debt repayments, family income needs, etc.) Total 'em up here.

Rent & Utilities	1500
Marketing	
EMR, Email, Phone	
Continuing Education, Sup o thumpy	
Supplies	1100
Family/Personal Income Needs	
Debt Repayments	
TOTAL:	

Total Monthly Expenses: $_____

- Multiply your "months of leave" number by your total monthly expenses. This is the total amount you'll want to save for parental leave.

Total Savings Needed: $_____

- How many months of income do you have between now and your last day of work? (for example, it's February now and I'm due in September, so... I plan to be working in March, April, May, June, July, and August: that makes 6 months).

Months to Save: _____

- Divide your total amount of savings needed by the number of months you have to save. This is the amount you will need to save each month.

Monthly Savings Needed Between Now and My Due Date: $_____

This is the minimum amount of money you need to save monthly in order to be minimally financially prepared for being out of work for parental leave. If this number feels like a piece of cake, take a breath and keep doing what you're doing.

Consider Your Options

If this number feels like a stretch, you might do other things to bring in income:

• work a little more in your second trimester (run another group, offer a workshop, do a little more of whatever kind of side-work you do best)

• pound that pavement to bring in more clients now (assuming you're using ethical decision-making about with whom you will work — more on this later.)

• make a plan for earning passive income during your leave (write a book, create an e-course, etc. etc. etc.)

• take out a personal loan

• plan to return to work earlier than you wanted (a last resort option!)

Your Thoughts

What's your plan? Any other ideas for bringing in more income that come to your mind?

_____

_____

_____

FIRST TRIMESTER

Short-Term Disability Insurance

Here's another idea altogether: purchase short-term disability insurance. If you are the owner of or employed by a group practice, purchasing voluntary short-term disability insurance for 3 or more employees might be a cost-effective way to prepare for maternity leave following a "normal" childbirth, for illness necessitating bed rest during pregnancy, or for medical complications following childbirth. That is, if the insurance plan is purchased prior to conception, and there are many more "ifs" and variables too.

If you are in a solo practice, purchasing an individual short-term disability plan might be a cost-effective way to prepare for the possibility of bed rest or postpartum medical complications, but will not cover lost income following a normal childbirth. Unfortunately for partners of pregnant people, you will not qualify for financial support via short-term disability insurance during your parental leave.

For more information, please check out the resources at the end of this book.

CHECKLIST + TIMELINE

Here's your first checklist! There's another one following the section on the second trimester and, you guessed it, one after the section on the third trimester. You might choose to plug some of the dates and tasks of these checklists into your calendar to set reminders, giving yourself some time to think about how things are going and what you want to do next.

___ Get more rest (I told you I wouldn't tell you to, but here I am...)

___ Break the coffee habit, quit smoking, and stop drinking

___ Buy a box of saltines, a bag of peppermints, and/or a couple of cans of peaches (a.k.a. bland food) to store in your office

___ Seek out nausea remedies (my fave was breathing slowly in and out and sipping on and smelling herbal teas)

___ Get a therapist and/or make a self-care plan

___ Make a financial plan for income and savings

Last Day of Your 1st Trimester: _____

SECOND TRIMESTER

"Birth is an opportunity to transcend. To rise above what we are accustomed to, reach deeper inside ourselves than we are familiar with, and to see not only what we are truly made of, but the strength we can access in and through birth."

Marcie Macari

Sometime Later:

Client Work in the Second Trimester

The second trimester begins at the 14th week of pregnancy and lasts until the end of the 27th week. Hopefully, you will see some relief from the woes of morning sickness and maybe even catch that second trimester burst of energy everybody's always talking about. During the second trimester, you have a lot of decisions to make about what's best for you, your growing baby, and each of your clients. After you announce your pregnancy, your clients' treatment plans will change a bit as you prepare them for you being away. Your second trimester is when the action of being a pregnant therapist will begin in your practice. You will talk with your clients about changes and time off, you will begin to process clinically the effect these changes might have, and you will make decisions about how much more work to take on, where to cut back, and when to stop. Let's think about these decisions and changes now as you get ready to take action.

When to tell clients that you're pregnant is a very personal decision. First, check in with yourself — how are you feeling about telling your clients? Think about both the act of making your pregnancy known to your clients and how you might feel about having your pregnancy known to your clients for many months. Some of your clients will not feel affected by your pregnancy; some will feel affected but won't seem that way; and some will be openly impacted and request to do a lot of processing. The fact of your pregnancy and the break in their treatment with you are unexpected changes to a client's treatment. Choosing when to tell your clients is not about keeping secrets; it's about balancing your own professional boundaries with the client's right to be the focus of their treatment.

Let's Break This Down:
Deciding When to Break the News

What is your average length of treatment of your clients? Your answer can guide when you tell current clients and potential clients and when you stop taking on new clients. If you typically see clients for less than 3 months, theoretically you could wait to disclose your pregnancy and continue taking on clients until into your third trimester, although that bump might begin to give you away.

Many of us treat clients for longer than 6 months. If that's the case for you, consider what can be accomplished in less than a couple of trimesters. Depending on the client's presenting issues, level of motivation, current resources, and your therapeutic model, it's possible that good work can be done in the short term: relationship-building, psycho-education, resource-building, problem-solving, etc. As long as potential clients are allowed to make a choice, you might decide to continue taking clients well into your second trimester.

Your last day of work should also factor in here. If you want to work right up until you go into labor (peace and blessings be upon you), maybe you've got more time before you'll want to break the news.

Question: When do I want to tell my current clients?

My Answer: Sometime between Week 14 and Week 28 and when it feels right in your gut. As soon as you tell current clients, your pregnancy and impending leave and all the uncertainty that might arise for clients will become something you will need to be aware of and to manage in the room. It's okay to not be ready, at the beginning of your second trimester, to be a pregnant person in your therapy office and to wait to tell clients until you're ready. It's probably not okay to tell clients right away just to get it off your chest and then to act like it's not a thing.

Your Answer:

_____

_____

Question: When do I want to tell potential clients?

My Answer: As soon as you begin to tell current clients, go ahead and work it into your potential client spiel too.

Your Answer:

_____

_____

Question: When do I want to stop taking on new clients?

My Answer: If you practice short-term therapy, you might choose to work up until the end, keeping in mind that due dates are great, but none of us ever really know when our pregnancy will end. If you practice long-term therapy, you might choose to stop taking new clients sometime between Week 14 and Week 26. You'll also want to balance your desire to keep working and earning with the reality that the further along you get in your pregnancy, the more tired and distracted you are likely to be.

Your Answer:

_____

_____

The moral of the story is: It's up to you, folks, and that marvelous gut wisdom of yours.

The Over-Share

When I was pregnant with my first, I was working both in private practice (my dream job) and in an agency (a very good job, but a monster of a commute). I knew there was a possibility that I might not return to the agency after my parental leave was over, but I also knew that I'd never been pregnant before and I'd never been a new mom before, and I wanted to make as few decisions as possible about a life I wasn't yet acquainted with. I believe in honesty, but I also believe that I don't always have all the answers to make good decisions, and I wasn't ready to let go of a good job. I chose to keep the agency job through parental leave and to postpone all decision-making about whether or not I would return or what my return to the agency would look like. I thought long and hard about the ways this uncertainty should influence what I say to clients, so that I could prepare them as much as possible.

The Impact of Your Pregnancy

The appearance of your belly and your disclosure of your pregnancy will have an impact both on your clients and on you. Your clients might feel more curious about your life and might ask more personal questions. They might feel resentful of you, afraid of losing you, jealous, more dependent, more withdrawn, more resistant, and/or more ambivalent. Pregnancy is a good time for regular individual and/or group supervision.

Pregnancy brings "stuff" up for all child-bearers - childhood stuff, relational stuff, emotional stuff, hormonal stuff, and trauma stuff. I'll tell you a secret. There were times during each of my pregnancies that I had the strangest, most desperate desire to be a baby myself — to have no responsibilities, to be cuddled by my partner like a baby, to be fed by him, and to be tucked in at night. Cullen-Drill (1994) puts it more clinically: "Often a pregnant woman 'regresses' to earlier wishes for dependency and fusion with the primary love object." (#yesindeed) Even if in the past we've done our own work on all of our "stuff", it's inevitable that this major change in our lives will require us to revisit old wounds and to seek out more healing.

If you are the partner of a pregnant person, your "stuff" will likely come up too (except maybe the hormonal stuff). Pregnant people and their partners might feel guilty about leaving their current clients and/or about taking on new clients prior to parental leave. You each might feel more afraid of losing clients both before and after your leave. You might feel distracted by your baby's presence in the room or existence in the womb of your partner and even resentful that you can't spend all of your time connecting with your little bean and preparing for their arrival. Fear, guilt, pride, excitement, the desire to conserve emotional resources — you just can't avoid being human during such a transformative time in your life.

Impending parenthood might also increase your intuition, empathy, and connection with your clients. It might inspire you to create more, to share more love, or even to do something wild like writing a book (*wink*). There's beauty in the darkness and in the light.

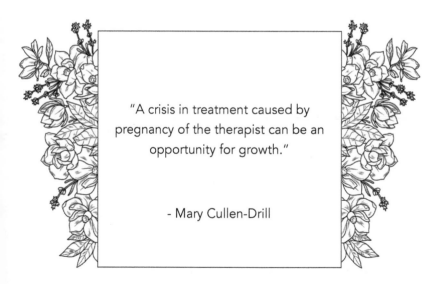

"A crisis in treatment caused by pregnancy of the therapist can be an opportunity for growth."

- Mary Cullen-Drill

<u>Let's Break This Down:</u>
The Announcement

Yes, you eventually have to tell your clients, but what do you say and how do you say it? Some things to think about, pre-announcement:

- no matter what model of therapy you practice, your personal life will become present in the room, a fact that might feel different for a psychoanalyst than for a somatic therapist (take some time to consider how this might feel for you and for your clients)

- keep it short and sweet (there's a lot you could say, prepare to say it clearly and briefly)

- don't leave out the sweet (it's okay to convey happiness, while at the same time anticipating and making room for how each client will take the news)

- identify your own feelings and accept them, before you announce (you might be having mixed feelings about this big change; listen to and take care of yourself)

The Nuts and Bolts of the Announcement

- give them the facts (you're pregnant ✓ & when you are due)

- address the inevitability of leave, when and for how long you plan to be away, & the possibility that plans will change (you might plan to take 3 months and decide while you're away that you need more... or less, #pleasedonttakeless)

- mention your intention to do transition planning (you don't need to know right away who you will refer them to, if that's even something they want, but do some foreshadowing)

- tell your clients about your expectation that this news will bring up feelings, questions, and issues

- ask your clients to track what comes up for them and set an intention to discuss it together

- read the room — if the client is smiling, crying, or appears nonplussed, let this guide the next thing you say

Your Spiel

Put it in your own words:

_____

_____

_____

_____

_____

_____

_____

_____

_____

_____

_____

_____

_____

_____

_____

_____

_____

_____

The Over-Share

Here's my pregnancy announcement spiel that I modified in ways depending on which client I was talking to:

> "I want you to know that I'm pregnant [do not pause too long here unless client bursts into shrieks of joy or pain] and due in some-such-month. I'm aware that this might bring up feelings, questions, or just 'stuff' for you. I'd like you to track what comes up for you and don't hesitate to discuss it with me. I plan to take 3 months of leave and we'll make a plan together for what my time away will look like for you. I also want you to know that there's the possibility that my availability will be different when I return and for that reason, I'd like us to use the next few months to say goodbye to each other and to celebrate the work we've done so far. Do you have any thoughts or questions?"

While delivering my spiel, I planned not to pause after the words, "I'm pregnant," because some clients are socialized to say, "congratulations," even when they might not feel celebratory. I didn't want my clients to feel like I expected a particular reaction from them.

Preparing For Post-Announcement

Before you go ahead with the announcement, consider the many issues that might affect a client's response to the news:

- client has a history of infertility and/or is actively participating in fertility treatment (this is hard stuff, y'all, physically and emotionally)

- client is actively trying to conceive (maybe it's taking longer than they expected)

- client is longing for children (maybe they haven't found a partner yet, maybe their partner doesn't want kids)

- client is a parent (maybe your pregnancy launches them into mentor-mode, maybe it elicits happy or painful memories of past pregnancies or the beginning of their parenthood)

- client isn't interested in becoming a parent (so, it's like, that's cool for you and everything, but moving on...)

- client has a history of multiple therapists, therapist turnover, and/or feeling abandoned or rejected (you are about to become another one of those people that has left them)

Take some time to think about each of your clients and how your announcement might land with them. Before you begin to make the announcement to each client, tune in to them.

The Over-Share

As it turned out, when I got pregnant a second time while self-employed in private practice, I used basically the same wording when announcing to clients. I'd never been the mother of two small children before either, and many postpartum variables are difficult to predict — the availability of childcare, the location of childcare, medical complications of birth for mothers and for babies, etc. — so I decided it was best for me to foreshadow that my future schedule might not remain the same.

Looking Ahead to the Fourth Trimester

It's true that one day, relatively soon, you will not be available to your business for a period of time while you're on parental leave. As you think about how long you plan to be away from your business, let's take a look at what you might be able to expect about your baby's life post-birth.

In the United States, maternity leave is offered either not at all or for a maximum of 3 months, a figure that was arrived at through political negotiations rather than research-based, expert opinion on what is best for babies and their caregivers. However, the first 3 months of a baby's life is a critical period in their development that is thought of as their fourth trimester of gestation.

Developmentally, in this fourth trimester, they need their environment to still be womb-like, but because the human brain is so big and the human birth canal is so small, our bodies eject them into the world at the end of the third trimester. If this is not your first rodeo, you've got some idea of how many needs a 0- to 3-month-old has. If this is your first baby, here are some needs to think about:

- the need to be touched, to be in close proximity with a limited number of primary caregivers (a parent, another parent, another carer; as few and as predictable as possible)

- the need to sleep often and on demand (and often while being touched)

- the need to be fed often and on demand (and always while being held and gazed at)

- the need to learn how to breastfeed (this applies to mamas and babies who are pursuing this route) — rooting, latching, sucking, colostrum, tongue-tie, let-down, supply, pumping, hand expressing, foremilk, hindmilk, engorgement, mastitis, cluster feeding, etc., oh my, oh my, oh my!

- the need to be attuned to and quickly — 0- to 3-month-olds can't auto-regulate or self-soothe, they only co-regulate with a primary caregiver, and every baby has a different temperament and different attunement needs

- the need to be comforted when crying — for some babies, crying might be their last-ditch effort at getting their need met if a caregiver hasn't been able to attune to their need, and some babies just cry a lot, whether they are being attuned to or not

- the need to feel safe as they develop their senses — think about what it's like to be all cozied up and warm in bed, covers pulled up to your ears in the dark and cold of your room in the morning, and then to have your alarm go off... and then to throw the covers off and feel that blast of cool air hit your body... and then to turn the lights on and feel your eyes squinting and pupils dilating... now imagine you don't know what "cold" or "light" means or what the heck an "alarm" is — an infant's world is constant exploration of the senses, and they depend on us and a neutral environment to feel safe

- the need to learn how to use their body — play and toys and tummy-time in a safe environment in close proximity to or direct connection with a caregiver

During the first 3 months of a baby's life, parents are typically at their most sleep-deprived and stressed. If you have a lot of daytime and nighttime support, this time might not phase you as much as if, like most American households, you and your partner are the only ones responsible for baby, cooking, cleaning, laundry, care of other children, etc. I just talked about baby's needs, but you've got needs too, whether you birthed the baby or not! You will be sleep-deprived and your body will be healing. Whether you have a vaginal delivery or cesarean delivery, medication-free labor, induced labor, or medicated labor, your body has just been through 9+ months of an exhausting ordeal and needs time to heal. Both parents going back to work anytime before baby is 3 months old is sometimes absolutely necessary and is also likely to add more stress to an already stressful time.

And then, there is... dare I say it... the possibility that you (and/or your partner) will experience postpartum mood and anxiety changes. It's not inevitable, but it's important to know that it can happen, even to mental health professionals. I had the baby blues at first — overwhelmed, anxious, and irritable — the things you'd expect a person to experience in the face of change with a healthy sprinkling of sleep deprivation. I sought out help when I started to notice a pattern of excessive crying, increased irritability, difficulty making decisions, and emotional collapse that often sounded like, "I don't want to be here anymore." It took me about a month to reach out for help from my best friend, who sat with me as I told my husband and we made a plan to call my doctor and my therapist. If you experience depression or anxiety in the postpartum period, you are not alone. Please check out the resources at the end of this book.

This is my plea: consider your personal and familial needs first before considering the needs of your business or clients. You aren't the only one who can help your clients, even though you are straight-up the best therapist out there and your clients love you and even though your clients have chronic and severe needs and fears of abandonment and you want to be there for them. They want to work with you AND you aren't the only one who can help them. But you and/or your partner are the best people to help this new little life adjust to the world outside the womb... just sayin'.

<u>Let's Break This Down:</u>
When to Carry On with the Business Of Your Business

Some of you might choose to take a break from your business altogether so you can devote your attention to healing your body, taking care of your family, and getting your baby acclimated to the world — a tough decision. Some of you might choose to continue to be available to your business in some capacity, part-time or full-time, balancing body, baby, and business — also a tough decision. As you might already know, there is no such thing as a balanced personal and professional life; no way to have everything in a perfect state of equilibrium all the time. There's only the act of balancing (or some might say it's more like juggling).

If this is your first pregnancy, it's true that there's a lot more in store for you than you have the capacity to prepare for or to expect. First time parents might benefit more from pulling further back from your business — taking more time away, not planning to check a single email or answer a single business-related phone call while you're away — and then reengaging as you feel ready, rather than planning to be more involved and then needing to step further back if things begin to feel like they're too much. But hey, who'm I kidding? The entirety of this paragraph also applies to second time parents and beyond. Ultimately, you've got to make the decision that feels right to you, then give yourself permission to evaluate how that decision is going along the way and to change course as you see fit.

Another aspect of carrying on with your practice despite your plan to take a parental leave is continuing to take on clients. A relatively new client relationship can absolutely bounce back from a three-month break, but that absolutely depends on some things:

1) the interest of a potential new client in beginning therapy with you knowing that in a few short months you'll be away on leave for a period of time (talking about informed consent, y'all)

2) your level of comfort with providing short-term services for a new client prior to your leave

3) the severity of the client's presenting problem and their service needs

Your Thoughts

What does your gut say as you ponder how much leave to plan for and how much you'll plan to engage with your business during your leave? How long will you plan to spend recovering? How does it feel to think about being away from your business for that long? How might sleepless nights, baby needs, medical complications, and/or postpartum depression or anxiety impact your engagement with your business and your return to work?

_____

_____

_____

_____

_____

_____

_____

What fears and/or concerns come up for you as you think about returning to work after your pregnancy? (for example: "I'm afraid my clients will forget about me if I'm gone for too long.")

_____

_____

_____

_____

_____

_____

_____

How old are these fears and where do they come from? (for example: "I feel like a 7-year-old when that fear comes up.")

_____

_____

_____

_____

_____

_____

What do these fears need to hear from you? (for example: "That fear needs to hear from me that I'm a competent person with a lot to offer.")

_____

_____

_____

_____

_____

The Over-Share

About halfway through parental leave with my first, I realized I could not go back to the agency. As I prepared to continue working only in my private practice and to do what was necessary to build it into a full-time business, I got to feeling overzealous about making my business work. I went back to private work after two-and-a-half months of leave and while true that it was only part-time, it was a struggle in many ways. It wasn't a decision I made for the best interests of myself and my family, it was a decision I made based on fear of not having enough money and of losing clients.

I remember, toward the middle of my pregnancy, talking to a group of female colleagues and telling them that I was planning to start seeing a few clients after two weeks, WEEKS!, postpartum. One by one around our circle, they gently suggested that I please don't do this, telling me their own stories of returning to work after having a child. Thank goodness I listened to them and did not do that original plan, but for me 2.5 months postpartum following an unplanned cesarean delivery was also way, way too soon.

Let's Break This Down: Talking with Potential Clients

Now that you've shared the news with your current clients, you're looking over your calendar and your short-term business goals and you see that you still have a few openings to fill. Whether you engage in some active marketing or networking strategies to drum up some new business or you sit back to see if any new business comes your way, here are some thoughts on what to say in that first call from a potential new client:

- you don't have to lead with your news ("Hello, potential client! First, you should know… I'm pregnant." *crickets chirping*)

- you're a professional, so begin the conversation as you usually would: what are their presenting issues? (and assuming you feel comfortable offering them short-term treatment…) how you'd like to offer support. can you agree upon an appointment time? do you take their insurance? do they accept your fee?

- if it feels like a good fit to you and the potential client, it's time to talk pregnancy and leave. give them a modified announcement spiel and then ask, "how does that sound?"

Your pregnancy and leave may un-sweeten the deal for a potential client, but there's no need to apologize for this and there's no way around it. It might be a deal breaker and that's okay. If you give them an idea of who you are and what you can offer before you discuss pregnancy and if that feels like a good fit to them, they might reach out to you at some future date. You never know. Your modeling of informed consent, healthy boundaries, and self-care can only enhance your business.

Your Potential Client Spiel

_____

_____

_____

_____

_____

_____

_____

_____

_____

_____

_____

The Over-Share

During my second pregnancy, I was contacted at the beginning of my second trimester by a potential client with chronic mental health issues that were having a serious impact on her functioning. I'd not yet told my current clients about my pregnancy and I had no plan to incorporate the disclosure into my calls with potential clients yet. The issues that this potential client spoke of were those that I feel competent to treat in a long-term capacity, but something didn't feel right. As I looked ahead to my plan for parental leave in just a few short months, it felt like her needs were greater than I was capable of offering care for at that time.

As I thanked her for sharing her story, I chose to tell her that while I typically treat her concerns, "in a few short months I will be out of the office for an extended period of time" and that it sounded like she needed more consistent care than I could provide. I told her I'd like to provide her with three referrals and she agreed.

I didn't tell her why I'd be away and she didn't ask. We focused right back in on getting her the support she needed.

Don't tell potential clients before you feel ready to tell (and have told) your current clients. Make it easy on yourself and wait until you're ready to deal with this dynamic openly and across the board.

When to Stop Taking New Clients

If less than 3 months is your average length of treatment, you might choose to stop taking on new clients towards the end of your second trimester, keeping in mind that your due date is not set in stone and you can never be certain when your baby will decide to be born.

If greater than 3 months is your average length of treatment, you guessed it — you might choose to stop taking on new clients even sooner. Whatever you decide, make sure you feel comfortable clinically supporting your decision (I'm talking about gut wisdom again that you can back up with clinical and ethical decision-making). Make sure your choice isn't motivated solely by your business' financial goals.

You might practice a long-term therapy and still expect that some progress can be made in the short-term (such as skill-building, resourcing, focusing on an achievable short-term goal, etc.). It's likely that you'll need to make this decision on a case by case basis as you make preliminary assessments of goodness of fit for each potential new client.

Control Is an Illusion, So Plan for Early Labor

Sure, you've got a due date. You've committed it to memory and when anyone/everyone asks, you faithfully respond. This is something you know, perhaps one of the few things. Except…babies don't know that we're already clocking them. They don't know that they are expected to arrive on September the 7th (much as I tried, I could not un-know this date). Some of them come later than the due date and some of them come sooner; most of them do not abide by medical timetables. Choosing when to stop working involves many different factors and there is no right answer. Some people plan to stop working before their due date and some plan to work until they go into labor. Medical complications, physical functioning challenges, and baby's own arrival plans sometimes disrupt our own ideas.

It can feel really hard to not know when you will go into labor and therefore when you want to stop working. Our work is appointment based direct service; our physical presence is essential to every meeting. During my first pregnancy, every single image I had in my mind about how birth begins involved an "uh-oh, my water just broke" exclamation and then a mad dash to the hospital with lots of screaming, breathing, and sweating. The vast majority of women do not experience their first births that way, but that did little to settle my nerves. I stopped working too early and the baby arrived two weeks late. I was boooooorrred. In hindsight, a better early labor plan might have settled me down enough to work a little longer.

If you go into labor after you've stopped seeing clients, your biggest "problems" might be anxious anticipation or boredom, if you're like me. (Most of you, I'm sure, will easily rest just like the midwife/doctor ordered, right?) For those babies who arrive before you planned to stop working, you will need to shift your focus from business to baby in an unexpected way. Let's make a plan for that.

Of course, you've already begun to plan for the unexpected — you've alerted your clients to the fact that you aren't in control of when the baby arrives. Now that you've informed your clients of your pregnancy and plans for taking leave, it's time to plan for early labor. No, you certainly hope it does not happen that way, but you are not in control. Control is an illusion.

Some action points:

- draft an email message that can be sent to active clients in the event that you go into labor before your planned last day of work

- choose a trusted colleague who is willing to send this email for you

- ask your clients to give you permission to share their name and email with this person by signing a release of information

Give this colleague the drafted email and a list of your clients and their preferred email addresses. If you use an EMR with secure email capability, you can grant this colleague administrative access to your clients so that they can contact clients via secure email. Pay special attention to two things: 1) that you are not giving this colleague access to more information than the client granted them permission to have, and 2) that you guard against improper use of email, which is NOT a confidential or HIPAA compliant form of communication. Secure email is always best.

If you must use email that is not secure, a BCC email or a separate email to each client and email contents devoid of any client protected health information (PHI) is essential. If you've already got an administrative assistant who can do all of these things for you, you rock my friend (#practicegoals). And please, for your clients' sakes and your own, have this trusted colleague or administrative assistant repeat this mantra before they begin, "I'm sending a BCC email. I'm sending a BCC email. I'm sending a BCC email." Be meticulous about this.

The Parental Leave Release of Info

The authorization for the release of information you ask your clients to sign should speak to the following points:

- permission to have contact info shared with a specific clinician for the purposes of conveying changes to your plan for leave due to labor and childbirth or any medical reason

- reiterating the timetable: due date, planned last day of work, planned date of your return to work, and the reality that things change

- spelling out expectations about the transition plan and the extent to which you will be reachable (or not!) during your leave

Making Big Decisions

Many lovely people gave me advice during my first pregnancy, and much of their advice I took because they were right, but they were right because they knew me. There are questions that can come across your desk during pregnancy or parental leave that might be hard to answer, such as: should I quit a job or a side hustle, change my hours, or work closer to home to be more available to my family or to be less stressed (a.k.a. more available to my family)? I've certainly provided a lot of advice in these pages, but the truth is, I know you are the best person to make decisions about your practice.

During your pregnancy, as you sift through your wants, fears, and needs in making big decisions, ask yourself, "Is the choice I'm exploring:

a) in line with my personal, professional, and/or financial goals?

b) in line with my values?

c) an attempt to avoid things that are hard or that I don't like?"

For example, if the choice you're exploring is whether to quit a job, but a) it's your professional goal to get two years of experience working with a certain group of people and you're only one year in, b) you value finishing what you start, but c) the physical experience of being pregnant is kicking your butt and affecting your work and you hate feeling mediocre, then you might choose not to quit that job, but to give yourself permission to be mediocre right now.

Pregnancy is hard for many or most of us — exhausting, stressful, and sometimes scary. Some of you are worker bees buzzing right along without a second thought and some of you will be looking at your life to determine what you can change or cut back on to get some relief. If the choice you're leaning toward falls into category (c), make sure there are other good reasons to make that choice, because you are about to begin one of the hardest undertakings of your life (read: the birth of your baby and the postpartum period). You deserve to believe about yourself that you can do hard things that are in line with your values and goals. Because, it's true.

CHECKLIST + TIMELINE

First Day of Your 2nd Trimester:

_____

___ Choose a last day of work

_____

___ Decide how long you'll be away on leave

_____

___ Break the news to your current clients

___ Begin to tell potential clients

___ Decide when to stop taking new clients

_____

___ Choose a colleague to notify clients in the event of early labor

_____

___ Collect signed releases of information

___ Draft an early labor notification email:

_____

_____

_____

___ Give colleague email list, email content, and access to your calendar

___ Record an outgoing voicemail that tells folks you're not taking new clients, such as:

_____

_____

_____

First Day of Your 3rd Trimester:

_____

Last Day of Work: _____

Your Due Date: _____

THIRD TRIMESTER

"You'll discover there's no 'right' way to be pregnant, give birth, or [parent] — there's only your way."

Erica Chidi Cohen

Nearing the End:

Wrapping Things Up in the Third Trimester

The third trimester begins at week 28 of pregnancy and lasts until you ain't pregnant anymore. During the next few months your body will grow, grow, grow and so will baby. Your practice will experience the opposite as you wind down your work with current clients, stop taking on new work, and finalize preparations for how clients will receive support while you are away.

Winding Down Your Clinical Work

In the last 8-10 weeks of your planned time in the office, your clients need the work to come to some sort of close. It's time to start terminating. You aren't likely to be able to open up new work with a client and bring it to some sort of resting place within these last few sessions. This time is best devoted to summarizing and reflecting on the work you've done, consolidating goals, tying up loose ends, celebrating gains, and saying goodbye. Even if you and your client plan to reconnect after your parental leave, there will be a new-ness to the relationship. You will be starting over at a new beginning point.

Clients need you to track this for them. Make a note in your calendar when you have 8-10 sessions left with weekly and with bi-weekly clients. Look at a calendar together; let them know when the countdown begins and how this will impact your work together. Foreshadow the need to say goodbye, even if it's not forever.

Reach out to any clients with whom you don't meet regularly or haven't met with in a while. Let them know what's going on, give them an opportunity to come in for a check-in, and give them an opportunity to choose whether they want to be contacted when you return or to have their case closed or made inactive.

Have I Talked Enough About Self-Care?

Did I talk about why it's important to take care of yourself? You are a model of self-care for your clients and for your child(ren). Fill up your tank first, not only because you deserve it, but because your clients can feel it when you are running on empty. Here are some more self-care ideas:

- get the sleep your body needs

- eat all the good foods

- move that body through walking, dancing, swimming, exercising

- get a physical adjustment through massage, chiropractic, acupuncture

- get a soul adjustment through meditation, church, connection with friends and family

- consolidate your office hours, renegotiate your schedule to add more breaks, and/or reduce your hours

- work the way you want to, not the way you think you have to

The Over-Share

As I exited the second trimester of my second pregnancy with a 2-year-old at home, I thought twice about how much I was working (see what I did there?). Fatigue was catching up with me and I felt more tired than I had ever been. At the time, I was working in my practice outside the home three days a week and chasing a rambunctious toddler around two to four days a week. Come to think of it, I was also heavily involved in beautification projects in and around our new-to-us, very old home. The pregnant-er I got, the tired-er I got.

A radical question presented itself to me: did I want to work less, have more down time, get "dressed" one less day per week? Yes! I did! I looked at my schedule and figured out how to consolidate and negotiate my way down to working two days per week

Generally, I don't like slowing down or saying no when there's work to be done. It's supremely uncomfortable for me (which I'm working on). But I did it anyway. It was a radical act of self-care and it grew me, because what my body needed was what my baby needed. Once my baby was born, I knew he would need all of me for as long as possible and I needed a full tank of gas to fuel my care of him. To continue the car metaphor — because when you're driving full speed and you slam on the brakes, you skid and spin and have a generally harder time of things. The moral of this story is: pump those brakes friends, in any way you can.

Termination

"Wait a minute, I'm not leaving my clients," you say? "I'm just taking a break. I don't want anyone to think I'm abandoning them or that this is an end. I'm coming back!"

If your plan is to take a good ol' American maternity leave and to return to your business and to your clients in around 3 months, of course you might have some resistance to the idea of terminating. If your clients understand that this is your plan too and are looking forward to your return, they also might wonder why in the heck you keep talking about "termination". Whether or not you plan to return, though, your leaving will be an ending.

And even when you do return, you will be different. You will be a new parent, or a new parent again. If you're doing it right, you will be tired. You will be needed in new ways and your emotional priorities will have shifted. You might be experiencing your own postpartum mood changes or you might be supporting a partner who is. Your body will be different. Your personal relationships will be different. For these reasons and perhaps many more, your relationship with each client might change.

It's also possible that, because of a variety of possibilities, you might not be able to reconnect with each client that wanted to return. Here are some reasons why re-connection doesn't always work:

- you don't come back working the same number of hours or on the same days and your availability doesn't match a client's (family responsibilities, childcare constraints... there's a lot to balance)

- they decide, while you're away, that they're doing pretty well without you (and, assuming it's clinically appropriate, good for them!)

- for unknown reasons, they just don't return your attempt to re-connect (if you love something, let it go...)

- and, you know, it's always possible that you will decide to take more time off or even not to come back (gasp! can't imagine a world in which you would choose not to do this work that you love or that you wouldn't want to jump right back into it in 3 months? another thing you can't accurately imagine: your world post-baby)

A lot can change in a few short months. When I went out of the office on parental leave with my second babe I balked at the idea of maintaining a 30-minute commute after returning to work. It was an incredibly tough decision in many ways, but I made the decision to move my practice closer to home. This predictably changed the desire of some of my clients to continue to work with me. I completely understood that when it happened and was thankful that we had said goodbye in some way.

When you talk with your clients about termination, be honest about your plans and intentions and about the reality that plans and circumstances might change.

Transitioning Clients to Other Providers

Offer to connect your clients with a provider who can see them in your absence. If they take you up on that offer, provide each of them with three referrals. Surely, it's fine if everyone does this differently: Maybe some of you will offer the same three referrals to each of your clients? Maybe some of you will offer one provider who will act as your backup? Maybe some of you will try to carefully match each of your clients and their referrals by presenting issue/specialty, insurance, hours of availability, and geographic location?

To me, what felt right was that different clients had different preferences and different needs, and so I adjusted my approach to transition-planning to match each client's need. Some clients chose to decline referrals and to take a break while I was away, and if I didn't have safety concerns, I didn't insist on referring. Some clients requested referrals, and I gave them names of therapists I knew who practiced similarly to me. Some clients needed to stay within the one type of insurance I accepted at the time, and I didn't personally know any therapists who accepted this insurance. For these clients, I requested referrals from some of my networks and acknowledged to the client the fact that I couldn't directly vouch for the referrals I was providing.

If a client for whom you do have safety concerns does not particularly wish to see anyone while you are away, it's time to whip out your trusty therapist backbone. You must disagree, recommend a transfer, and provide referrals. And then document, document, document your conversations and recommendations regarding transfer.

It's always possible that you will refer a client to other providers and they will not follow up and schedule with anyone. Document your efforts and allow for client self-determination. It's always possible that a client will transfer to another provider and then choose not to return to working with you. Don't take it personally. Your leave will cause a certain amount of upheaval for each of your clients and everyone will handle that differently. Upheaval is the nature of pregnancy and it's the nature of life; change doesn't happen without it and without change, we don't grow.

When to Transition

This is yet another thing that will differ for each client. Some of them might need some overlap, where they continue to see you and begin to meet a new therapist at the same time. Whatever the case, encourage your clients who intend to transition to reach out to their referrals ASAP or offer to reach out for them; other therapists have waitlists, costs that are different from yours, and/or limits to their availability.

Documentation

You know what you need to do. Make sure all your progress notes are in, treatment plans are up to date, and transition plans or discharge summaries and recommendations are documented in each client's record. Document in a timely way, especially toward the end of your pregnancy, when your availability to complete administrative work becomes a little less predictable.

That was originally all I was going to write on the matter, but, in case you're not really sure what you need to do, here are some standards for documentation, from this social worker's perspective. Documentation includes client symptoms, functional status, diagnoses, treatment plan, progress notes, medications, and psychological and pertinent medical test results, as well as frequency of treatment, therapist's assessment, and modalities used. All of this documentation creates a client's medical record. Keeping medical records is the law, it is ethical, it is good self-care, and it's required by insurance companies.

Keeping medical records is the law. In Maryland, where I practice, the Code of Maryland Regulations (COMAR) states: "a health care provider shall maintain medical records for all patients in the health care provider's care for a minimum of 5 years after the medical record is made or until the patient is 21 years old, whichever is longer."

Keeping medical records is ethical (NASW, 2017). When you see a new client, what questions do you ask: What's the problem? How can I help? Then eventually, is it working? Are we done? Documentation helps you clarify the answers to these questions and more so that your treatment course is clear to you. It will also allow for continuity of care in the future if the client has terminated with you and then returns or begins to see a new clinician that wants to consult with you about their past care.

Keeping medical records is good self-care. Documenting your treatment efforts can help you respond to a malpractice lawsuit, though rare (knock on wood). Keeping detailed notes any time you conduct a risk assessment or a client makes a complaint against you will help you defend your clinical decision-making should legal action be taken against you. If you are away from your clients for a period of time on parental leave, coming back to your work and the documentation you kept will help you ease back in to your work by minimizing the effects of "mom brain"/"dad brain".

Keeping medical records is required by insurance companies, whether you are in-network or not. If you are in-network with one or more insurance companies, your contracts require you to keep medical records that prove medical necessity of your services and you may be subject to audits. Proving medical necessity means documenting that the client meets the criteria of a diagnosis and shows impaired functioning as a result of that diagnosis, and demonstrating how the services you're providing are meeting the client's treatment needs. Even if you are an out-of-network provider, your client may choose to use their insurance to seek reimbursement for your services. If they do, there's no doubt that at some point in time you will be asked to provide some documentation.

Your Last Day of Work

Plan ahead that your last day is some date that is, to you, reasonably ahead of your due date. This will give you some time to finish up administrative work and to breathe. Planning to work right up until you go into labor will appeal to some of you who are shooting for a specific earning goal or who are straight up workaholics (you know who you are). I have an opinion against the latter, because it doesn't allow for the importance of closure for our clients. Assuming you will designate a last day of work, let's plan for that.

Treat the last session with each client prior to your leave like it's the last session you may ever have with your client. It might not be...okay, I know! You're not abandoning your clients! But isn't it nice to sit down with someone and tell them all about how you've watched them grow over the course of your work together? Isn't it nice to reflect, perhaps after they've completed that nurturing, supportive art therapy project they've been working on the past four sessions? Doesn't it feel good to savor what has been working while exploring goals and intentions for the future? Or even to not have an agenda other than just to be with each other? Endings and goodbyes are just as important as beginnings.

Give each of your clients something of you to take with them, whether that's something you create together, something they create while with you, or an experience of cherishing the relationship you've created. During my first pregnancy, one client worked on a project where she wrote meaningful notes to herself about the work she had done thus far in therapy and the things she had learned. At her last session, she read them each out loud, we talked about them, and then she folded them up and placed them inside a small glass jar. During my second pregnancy, I purchased some printable mandala art prints and wrote a meaningful note to each client on the back. Some beautiful blank greeting cards would have also worked nicely. This was my personal choice and it felt right to me, but as always, make choices based on what feels right and appropriate to yourself, your clients, and to your way of working.

"How are you doing?"

Many people will ask you when you are due and what you are having. Hopefully, you'll have just enough people in your life checking in with you about how you're feeling throughout your pregnancy. Hopefully too, you will feel pretty good throughout, but this is rare (sorry). What is more likely is that you will sometimes feel good, excited, and emotionally steady, and sometimes feel lousy, scared, and emotionally dysregulated (thanks, hormones!). Your partner will bring home what had been your favorite pizza to share together, covered in sausage, lump crabmeat, crawfish, jalapeños, and Old Bay (we live in Maryland, y'all) and you will feel nauseous and burst into tears about how no one really cares about what you need (true story, don't judge). Pregnancy is physically and emotionally exhausting.

Even those of us who are doing okay could probably use more rest. Some of you will experience medical complications of your pregnancy and get clear directions from your doctor: bed rest. For those of you who will deal with fatigue, back pain, and other, less-medical pregnancy-related issues, what if you gave yourself permission to rest more?

Women are bombarded by messages that they should keep up their appearance and pace of life while pregnant, pop out a baby, lose that birth weight, and get right back to work. These internalized messages can devastate folks who can't achieve the ideal. Maybe we can practice what we preach to our clients about self-acceptance, self-care, and self-love. I hope you find ways to be gentle with yourself.

Let the tears flow! There is joy right behind them and every other emotion under the sun.

CHECKLIST + TIMELINE

First Day of Your 3rd Trimester:

_____

___ Create a referral list for each client

___ Reach out to active clients who aren't regularly scheduled

Your Date to Start Terminating: _____

___ Talk with each client about the timeline and plan for termination @ 8-10 weeks remaining

___ Provide referrals and make plans for transition

___ Document, document, document

Last Day of Work: _____

___ Outgoing voicemail that you're out on leave and email away message

Due Date: _____

"Let choice whisper in your ear and love murmur in your heart. Be ready. Here comes life."

Maya Angelou

FOR YOU, THE BEGINNING...

Conclusion

Writing this book helped me organize my thoughts and plans and I hope it helps you too. I hope you use this as a guide, and that you remember: your best guide is usually your gut. This is true for all the books you read and decisions you make during pregnancy. It's especially true for parenting. Care for yourself, gather information, and then tune in to your gut wisdom to help you decide.

We've come to the end of this book, but it's only the beginning for you in many ways. May you be safe. May you be healthy. May you be well cared-for. May you be loved. May your family be safe. May they be healthy. May they be well cared-for. May they be loved.

APPENDIX

RESOURCES

Please visit www.TheTherapistsGuidetoBeingPregnant.com for links to the resources below.

Coping with Pregnancy Loss

American Pregnancy Association. (n.d.) After a miscarriage: Surviving emotionally. Retrieved from https://americanpregnancy.org/pregnancy-loss/miscarriage-surviving-emotionally/

This page talks about grief, healing, and possible gender differences in grieving behaviors.

March of Dimes. (n.d.) Dealing with grief after the death of your baby. Retrieved from https://www.marchofdimes.org/complications/dealing-with-grief-after-the-death-of-your-baby.aspx

This page talks about grief, healing, possible gender differences in grieving behaviors, and thoughts on how children grieve.

Danielle, B. (2018, December 6). 'It's different for black women': The realities of our struggle with miscarriages.

Essence. Retrieved from https://www.essence.com/lifestyle/parenting/coping-black-women-miscarriage/

This article acknowledges the prevalence of miscarriage, the importance of processing loss, and the unique impact of miscarriage on Black women.

McAfee, E.M. (n.d.) Sisters in loss: Miscarriage, pregnancy loss, & infertility stories [Audio podcast]. Retrieved from http://www.ericammcafee.com

This podcast features conversations facilitated by Erica McAfee with women who have experienced pregnancy loss and infertility.

Self-Care On a Budget

Derkson, R. (2017, June 7). 11 Self care examples to revitalize your soul [Web log post]. Retrieved from https://www.thebewitchinkitchen.com/self-care-examples/

This blog post lists some free self-care ideas.

Petitjean-Barkulis, C. (n.d.) How to focus on self-care during pregnancy [Web log post]. Retrieved from https://www.mother.ly/lifestyle/focus-self-care-pregnancy

This blog post is going to market to you like crazy, but it also has a few fantastic and free self-care tips.

Unplanned Pregnancy

Office On Women's Health, U.S. Department of Health & Human Services. (n.d.) Unplanned pregnancy. Retrieved from https://www.womenshealth.gov/pregnancy/you-get-pregnant/unplanned-pregnancy

This page talks about ways to move forward as you consider your options, as well as addressing partner abuse.

Planned Parenthood. (n.d.) Pregnancy options. Retrieved from https://www.plannedparenthood.org/learn/pregnancy/pregnancy-options

This page talks about the three ways to handle an unplanned pregnancy and discusses how to decide what's best for you.

Postpartum Depression

Mayo Clinic. (n.d.) Postpartum depression. Retrieved from https://www.mayoclinic.org/diseases-conditions/postpartum-depression/symptoms-causes/syc-20376617

This page lists the symptoms of baby blues, postpartum depression, postpartum psychosis, and talks about postpartum depression for partners, when to see a doctor, causes, risk factors, complications, and prevention.

Postpartum Support International. (n.d.) Help for moms. Retrieved from https://www.postpartum.net/get-help/help-for-moms/

This page details various online and telephone resources for finding support for postpartum depression/anxiety. Partners experience postpartum mental health issues too.

Postpartum Support International. (n.d.) Tips for postpartum dads and partners. Retrieved from https://www.postpartum.net/get-help/family/tips-for-postpartum-dads-and-partners/

This page talks about how to recognize symptoms of postpartum depression and anxiety, how to help and support a partner who is struggling, and ways to take care of yourself.

Short Term Disability Insurance

Haney, K. (2019, February 21). Short-term disability pregnancy medical reasons [Web log post]. Retrieved from https://www.growingfamilybenefits.com/short-term-disability-pregnancy/

This blog post defines terms related to short-term disability insurance and explains what is and isn't covered by most plans.

Sachon, L. (2019, May 9). What to know about disability insurance and pregnancy. Retrieved from https://www.policygenius.com/disability-insurance/what-to-know-about-disability-insurance-and-pregnancy/

This article describes how short-term and long-term disability insurance plans typically work.

General Mother-/Parenthood Resources

Sacks, A. (n.d.) Motherhood sessions [Audio podcast]. Retrieved from https://www.alexandrasacksmd.com/

This podcast features therapy sessions conducted by Dr. Alexandra Sacks with mothers and covers a variety of topics related to motherhood.

Human Rights Campaign. (n.d.) Explore: Parenting. Retrieved from https://www.hrc.org/explore/topic/parenting

This page links to current resources regarding issues faced by LGBTQ-headed families.

Fantastic Private Practice Resources

Abundance Practice-Building, Allison Puryear. https://abundancepracticebuilding.com/

This website and its blog offers all kinds of tips for building your private practice. And she's funny, too.

QA Prep, Maelisa Hall. https://www.qaprep.com

This website and its blog offers really helpful tips and
answers to common and not so common questions
about all things paperwork.

REFERENCES

American Pregnancy Association. (n.d.). Fetal development: Second trimester. Retrieved from https://americanpregnancy.org/while-pregnant/second-trimester/

Caron, C. (2018, July 11). A survival guide for the fourth trimester: Practical suggestions for women dealing with the surprising things that happen to their bodies in the first months after childbirth. The New York Times. Retrieved from https://www.nytimes.com/2018/07/11/well/a-survival-guide-for-the-fourth-trimester.html

COMAR, Annotated Code of Maryland §10.01.16.04, Maintenance of medical records.

Cullen-Drill, M. (1994). The pregnant therapist. Perspectives in Psychiatric Care, 30(4), 7-13.

Gerber, J. (2005, July 21). The pregnant therapist: Caring for yourself while working with clients. Retrieved from https://www.apaservices.org/practice/ce/self-care/pregnancy

Gerson, B. (1994). An analyst's pregnancy loss and its effect on treatment disruption and growth. Psychoanalytic Dialogues, 4(1), 1-17.

Guy, J.D., Guy, M.P., & Liaboe, G.P. (1986). First pregnancy: Therapeutic issues for both female and male psychotherapists. Psychotherapy 23(2), 297-302.

Hall, M. (2014, April 8). What is medical necessity and why do I care? [Web log post]. Retrieved from https://www.qaprep.com/blog/2014/04/09/what-is-medical-necessity-and-why-do-i-care

Hall, M. (2014, May 4). Why medical necessity is important to private pay therapists [Web log post]. Retrieved from https://apastyle.apa.org/learn/quick-guide-on-references#Websites

Haney, K. (2019, February 21). Short-term disability pregnancy medical reasons [Web log post]. Retrieved from https://www.growingfamilybenefits.com/short-term-disability-pregnancy/

Haney, K. (2019, January 18). Short-term disability insurance for self-employed [Web log post]. Retrieved from https://www.growingfamilybenefits.com/self-employed-short-term-disability-insurance/

Kurtz, R. (2015). Body-centered psychotherapy: The Hakomi method (updated ed.). Mendocino, CA: LifeRhythm.

National Association of Social Workers. (2017). NASW code of ethics. §3.04 Client records. Retrieved from https://socialwork.utexas.edu/dl/files/academic-programs/other/nasw-code-of-ethics.pdf

Puryear, A. (2015, August 24). Pregnancy and maternity leave in private practice: Everything you need to know [Web log post]. Retrieved from https://abundancepracticebuilding.com/mindset/pregnancy-maternity-leave-private-practice-everything-you-need-to-know/

Ruíz, R. (2015, January 25). No family left behind: America's current maternal policy has nothing to do with families and everything to do with politics. Retrieved from https://mashable.com/2015/01/25/maternity-leave-policy-united-states/

U.S. Department of Health and Human Services Office for Civil Rights. (n.d.). HIPAA privacy rule and sharing information related to mental health. Retrieved from https://www.hhs.gov/sites/default/files/hipaa-privacy-rule-and-sharing-info-related-to-mental-health.pdf

U.S. Department of Health and Human Services Office on Women's Health. (n.d.) Pregnancy loss. Retrieved from https://www.womenshealth.gov/pregnancy/youre-pregnant-now-what/pregnancy-loss

Your baby and the fourth trimester. (n.d.). Retrieved from https://www.babycentre.co.uk/a25019365/your-baby-and-the-fourth-trimester

Your guide to the second trimester of pregnancy. (n.d.). Retrieved from https://www.whattoexpect.com/second-trimester-of-pregnancy.aspx

Your guide to the third trimester of pregnancy. (n.d.). Retrieved from https://www.whattoexpect.com/third-trimester-of-pregnancy.aspx

Zucker, J. (2015, April 28). The pregnant therapist. The New York Times. Retrieved from https://opinionator.blogs.nytimes.com/2015/04/28/the-pregnant-therapist/?smid=tw-NYTOpinionator&seid=auto&fbclid=IwAR3yBucINizGgVm_RI-2JWPAIjkUG3&mtrref=undefined&gwh=C8E8A3E2B-CBBDBA13CF194DF6C26CFF6&gwt=pay&assetType=REGIWALL